INTRODUCTION TO THE VALLEY OF ROCKS

Ideally, on a warm dry day it is anticipated th   vhere
you can spend a little time reading something   >ring
its landscape. A small glossary explains som   ome
across if you read the boxes of finer print   :ing
immediately then turn to page eight.

It is possible that you are not overcome with   ..ic sublime which Dr
Manton experienced (page one), nor do you ..... ine prospect quite as uncommonly
grotesque as did the Rev. Polwhele. Is it the landscape that has changed or our
sensibilities? Whatever else has changed, a sense of drama remains. It excites the
imagination and prompts a search for explanations both for the strange cyclopean rock
formations and the broad majestic sweep of the dry steep-sided valley. You might like to
consider some explanations of your own before you read on.

How it got there.   **Some early suggestions**

*"From Linton an easy and little descent led me to the Valley of Stones. The range of
hills here next to the sea are completely stripped of their soil, the bones only of the
earth remain; in the vale, stone upon stone is scattered, and the fern grows among
them. Its origin I can only conjecture. Water to have overwhelmed such a height must
have inundated all the lower country, a thing evidently impossible: and the hills on the
other side of the valley, not an arrow's flight distance, are clothed with herbage. A
water spout perhaps; but I am, to my shame, no naturalist, and must hypothesise as a
poet.*

*Was it the work of our giants, of the race of Albion? We have historic proof that they
were not large limbed enough,... I conceive it, therefore..... to be the ruins of some work
erected by the devil.... and this diabolical origin accounts why the process of nature in
clothing the rocks does not proceed here beyond a luxuriance of lichens."*

(Robert Southey, 1799)

*"...from top to bottom a wilderness of bare spiky uplifted strata, and shaly sliding
stones, and a mass of immovable boulders, strewn and tossed and scattered in
inconceivable confusion. Surely some mighty Northern Ice-King did a long day's sowing
and harrowing on this hillside in the days that are no more!*

*"How it 'got there' is more than I should like to settle with any pretence of dogmatic
security - though I have theories on the subject of the glacial epoch, thinking that I can
see the traces of the icebergs which dropped huge quartz boulders along the hills of
Devonshire,..."*   (George Tugwell, 1863)

Overleaf are two more recent ideas concerning the origins of this remarkable valley.

Why is the Valley of Rocks dry? (Idea One: Glacial diversion)

Where did the water come from?

As can be seen from the first viewpoint, the gradient of the valley floor suggests a stream flowing from the east, so perhaps explanation for the dry valley may be found upstream? It is clear both from the map opposite and from the air photo (page 2) that Lynton also stands in part of the same streamless valley. However, projecting the valley further upstream (beyond Lynton) has its problems, for although on a map the course of the Valley of Rocks seems to be a natural continuation of the East Lyn valley, the dry valley at Lynton is perched 145 metres (475 feet) above the mouth of the River Lyn at Lynmouth. How could the water of the East Lyn ever have flowed through the Valley of Rocks?

A dam?

If one were to build a dam some 150 metres high at Lynmouth, a deep lake would quickly form (and Lynmouth would drown!). The lake would eventually overflow along the lowest watershed, today the Valley of Rocks. Could a 'natural' dam in the past have created such a situation?

A landslide barrier of such proportions seems unlikely, but an ice wall is a different matter. Oscillations in climate over the last two million years have periodically produced vast ice sheets which probed south across the British Isles. The last great ice advance, only 18,000 years ago, reached south as far as the Welsh coast at Swansea.

An ice margin channel?

The maximum extent of ice in the British Isles occurred during an earlier glacial oscillation of unknown date but perhaps as much as 450,000 years ago (see page 44). This ice sheet deposited characteristic debris (*till*) in Somerset, dammed the Somerset levels and created a lake which overflowed southwards to the English Channel. To the west, evidence of *erratics* suggests that the ice might have been deep enough (thicker than 80 metres) to override Baggy Point as it thrust into the Taw-Torridge estuary as far as Barnstaple (evidence from *till*). At its maximum extent this ice sheet may well have abutted against the northern flank of Southwest England from the Mendips to the Scilly Isles. Ramped against Exmoor it could have ponded the Lyn, whose trapped waters might have escaped along the coast, utilising any convenient route available.

By virtue of the great volumes of water they carry at certain times of the year, such 'meltwater channels' on the margins of ice sheets today are characterised by having wide flat floors and steep sides. When abandoned by meltwaters these channels are frequently left high and dry and may cut across present-day drainage patterns. Attention has been drawn to the similarity of shape between the Valley of Rocks and known former meltwater channels in Wales and elsewhere. However, you may wish to be presented with more concrete evidence before committing yourself to this theory?

THE GLACIAL THEORY

(a) It is possible that a thick ice sheet once pressed against the northern margin of Exmoor, obstructing the natural mouth of the River Lyn and causing a lake to form. Blocked by the high wall of ice to the north, the Lyn might have overflowed along the coast. Rushing meltwaters could quickly carve a new deep steep-sided valley where none existed before.

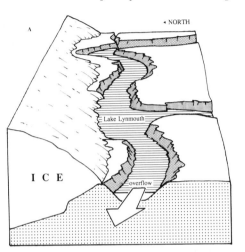

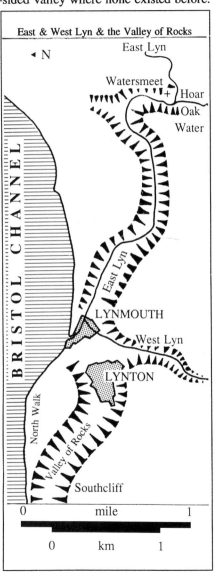

East & West Lyn & the Valley of Rocks

(b) When a warmer climate returned, the ice sheet melted. The Lyn reverted to its original course leaving the Valley of Rocks dry, perched high overlooking the Exmoor coast.

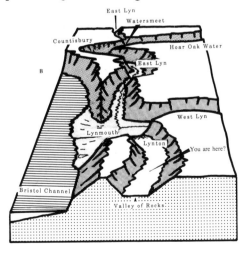

5

Why is the Valley of Rocks dry? (Idea Two: Coastal erosion)

Stream downcutting over time

A walk on the flanks of Exmoor makes it clear that streams here are very active. Not only is there evidence of a great deal of rock debris which is on the move when the stream is in flood, but steep gradients provide energy for these streams vigorously to erode their beds. Over time, valleys have become deeply entrenched into the landscape. For example the East Lyn River has cut a gorge some 200 metres (600 feet) deep and is still actively eroding its floor.

The time scale is such that it is very difficult to estimate the rate of downcutting. Yet we can imagine a time (possibly some 125,000 years ago) when the East and West Lyn were much less deeply incised into the upland surface, here a plateau with rounded summits swelling to about 300 metres (1000 feet). For example, remnants of old valley shoulders near Watersmeet, hint that the valley here may once have been entrenched about 85 metres (265 feet) into the plateau surface, instead of the 250 metres it is today. Thus, further downstream, the junction of the East and West Lyn could have been, at that time, more or less at the same altitude that Lynton and the Valley of Rocks stand today.

It may therefore be suggested that the site of Lynton and the Valley of Rocks was simply the lower course of the Lyn which at that time would have entered the sea further west (Stage A).

Erosion of the sea cliffs

Stage A shows the coast as it once might have been, well to the seaward of its present position. It is postulated that, during the last interglacial (see page 44), marine erosion of this coast eventually breached the seaward side of the Lyn valley near the site of Lynmouth, diverting or capturing the East and West Lyn by allowing them to cascade directly down to the shore. The beheaded lower course of the river would be left as a dry 'fossil' valley. The steep gradient at the point of capture, which may initially have been a spectacular waterfall, accelerated rapid downcutting by both rivers. As the East and West Lyn continued to deepen their valleys, the abandoned, dry valley floor was left perched relatively higher and higher above the active rivers. Today, Lynton, at the eastern end of the dry valley system, sits some 145 metres above the present floor of the East Lyn.

As you might suspect by the way the East Lyn and West Lyn tumble out of their valleys into Lynmouth the process of downcutting is far from complete. Coarse debris eroded by these rivers becomes part of the vast apron of stones called the Lynmouth delta. Stage B shows the coast as it appears today.

Which idea do you prefer?

There is no conclusive proof that either of these hypotheses are correct. Which sounds the most credible to you, glaciation or marine erosion, or have you a better idea of your own? We can return to these ideas later in the walk.

THE COASTAL EROSION THEORY

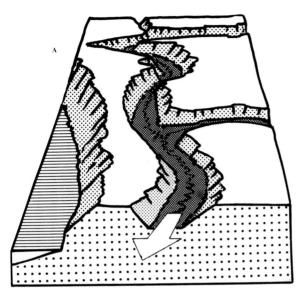

Stage A
The coast, looking east, as it might have appeared 125,000 years ago when the coastline was further north and the river valleys were not as deep. It implies that at that time the Valley of Rocks was part of the Lyn valley which had its mouth further west.

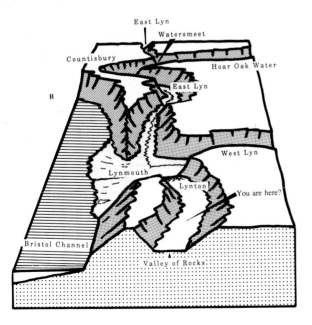

Stage B
Subsequently the sea could have eroded cliffs until the side of the Lyn valley was breached. As a result, the Lyn found a new way to the sea leaving its old lower course dry. The East and West Lyn cut gorges to the sea with renewed vigour.

STARTING THE WALK

The walk begins at the National Park picnic area and car park at the eastern end of the valley (see rear cover map). Directions to each viewpoint and a straightforward commentary are in bold print. Blocks of finer print offer more detailed notes of interest which can be referred to as you wish.

1 SUMMERHOUSE PATH

Cross the road. Take the path next to the small summerhouse, pausing to look down the valley when you are approximately at the location of the artist, G. Townsend, who was drawing here in about 1860. Has the valley changed much since those days?

Continue to walk towards the sea until you can inspect some of the bare rock exposed just before the path crosses the rocky ridge to descend to the North Walk. These rocks are part of the Lynton Beds.

2 ON THE ROCKS

Notice how the rocks are made up of many thin layers of sediment. These were *beds* of MUD, SILT and SAND, laid down on the floor of a warm shallow sea, some 395 million years ago. In time, these soft sediments were buried and compacted into MUDSTONES, SILTSTONES and SANDSTONES. Disturbances in the earth's crust further compressed the rocks, changing some into harder slates and folding many of the beds. Later, as the rocks were uplifted towards the surface and exposed by erosion, the resultant release of pressure encouraged the development of vertical fractures (joints).

The hard local sandstone is particularly resistant to *weathering* because joints, and those *bedding-planes* which are vulnerable to weathering, are widely spaced.

Nevertheless, wherever water or air could penetrate along the joints, the sandstone will have been weathered underground into massive rectangular blocks. When eventually exposed, such resistant 'building blocks' become tors. Locally the sandstone beds lie in a near-horizontal position, emphasising the tabular nature of the blocks piled one on another.

Knowledge of these rocks is the result of years of study in many locations. However, even on a casual visit, evidence suggesting where these rocks were formed, what was living in them at the time and how the rocks responded to intense pressure when they were buried deep underground, lies all about. The panel, on page 11, illustrates some of the 'evidence' you might like to look out for during your walk.

The local rocks

The Lynton Beds or Lynton Slates

During the Devonian Period (395-345 million years ago) this part of the Earth's crust was located some 20 degrees south of the equator (roughly on the latitude of the Kalahari Desert today). A large desert continent (the Old Red Sandstone Continent) extended over areas which are now South Wales and beyond through Scotland. North Devon lay on the edge of this continent. At times this tropical desert stretched into North Devon depositing riverine sediments on a wide coastal plain, with sands reddened with haematite from the oxidation of iron compounds in the hot desert. At other times North Devon was beneath the sea, but still receiving the products of the belching rivers, heavy with material easily eroded from the bare desert environment.

The Lynton Beds represent the first recognised episode when shallow seas flooded the margin of this warm red continent, depositing marine sediments of what were to become mudstones, siltstones and fine-grained sandstones. Even when thick beds of sand were forming they were often interrupted by thin laminae of fine clays and silts, suggesting periods of undisturbed waters between stormy periods when sand beds were disturbed by wave **ripple marks** (see opposite).

There are occasional thin beds of pale brownish limestone with **shell beds** (see opposite), including brachiopods, and crinoidal debris. Although the shells may be broken and distorted they can be identified and provide evidence of the shallow warm marine conditions in which these rocks formed. Animals which inhabited the soft sediments often severely disturbed the beds (bioturbation), and *trace fossils*, such as the remains of tunnels left by burrowing animals, may be found.

Mountain Building

Around 300 million years ago, all the Devonian and Carboniferous rocks of North Devon were deformed by pressure which caused folding and faulting and threw up a chain of mountains across the south-west peninsula (the Variscan *Orogeny*). However, this folding is not very evident in the Valley of Rocks, for here the beds are near-horizontal, representing the flat top to a large fold having a wavelength of several kilometres. The beds here dip gently (7 degrees) towards the east. Nevertheless the Lynton Beds were radically modified by the orogeny. Some mudstones were metamorphosed into slates with a strong cleavage and indeed the most recent geological memoirs for the district prefer to call the local rock formation the Lynton Slates rather than the Lynton Beds.

Confirmation that these beds were affected by powerful distorting pressures may be found by examining the planes between the beds. Some of these beds will show signs of **slickenside** (see opposite), evidence that these sheets of rock once slid over one another to compensate for lateral pressure during folding.

EVIDENCE IN THE ROCKS

RIPPLE MARKS

Ripple marks are formed on the surface of soft sediments by currents. If the ripples are symmetrical this suggests there were oscillatory currents caused by waves in shallow water. Asymmetric ripples are formed by a current running in one direction and will exhibit cross bedding when seen in section. ▸

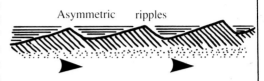

Asymmetric ripples

FOSSIL SHELL BEDS

These can occur in thin pale limestone bands which often weather out faster than the harder sandstones, so may be found in shadowy nooks such as the base of the Cheesewring or beneath the rock overhanging the start of the path up Castle Rock (see later). Recognition of shell species gives evidence of the warm marine conditions in which many of these sediments were laid down and allows the rock to be dated. You may also find fragments of sea lilies (crinoids), relatives of sea urchins and starfish. ▸

SLICKENSIDES

When beds of rock are folded they may develop scratches on the bedding planes of the folded rock. Bend this booklet slowly into a U-shape and notice how the pages move against one another as they adjust to the new structure. The marks on the bedding surfaces, called 'slickensides' or 'stretching lineations', were formed by similar adjustments as the rock layers slid over one another as they formed folds or faults. There may also be some 'streaked-out' pale quartz along the junction which was remobilised as a result of solution during deformation.

If you rub your finger along the 'scratch', one direction should feel rough and the other smooth. The 'smooth' direction is the direction of movement of the overlying bed. If found on a fault plane surface, slickensides can similarly indicate the direction of movement of the fault.

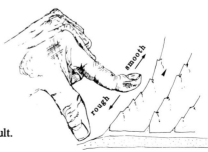

11

The North Walk from the air (1988). Can you locate your (perilous!) position? Many clefts and caves, here exposed at low tide, pierce the cliff below you.

3 NORTH WALK

From the col the path drops diagonally across the seaward slope which precipitously slides towards the sea but within a minute meets a more level track contouring the hillside out from Lynton. Turn left (west) along the track and pause.

This is the North Walk, engineered by a Mr Sanford in 1817 as a commercial venture. The first hotel in Lynton had been built only ten years before and walks suitable for the new genteel, romantic, scenic tourists were in demand. An early guide found it necessary to assure the visitor that the path was well-built into the cliff and that *"there is little occasion for giddiness"*. Noting the excellent views across to Wales, it drew visitors' attention to the *"smoke wreaths of Swansea"*, referring to the smelting works of that town. Thomas Henry Cooper, writing in 1853, described it as *"one of the finest terrace walks imaginable."*

The cliff traversed by the North Walk has a steep vegetated slope, hanging above the sea, and is better described as a seaward-slope rather than a true sea cliff, for only the very bottom of the slope is fresh-faced cliff. At low tide, a rocky shore platform is exposed, but at high tide the cliff foot is attacked by waves, which puncture less resistant parts of the face with clefts and caverns.

Tarka the Otter   (Henry Williamson, 1927)

"Swimming towards the sunset (from Lynmouth) Tarka found a cleft in the high curved red cliff, and on the crest of a wave rode into the cavern beyond. The broken wave slapped against the dark end as he climbed to a ledge far above the lipping of the swell, and curled himself on the cold stone. He awoke when the gulls and cormorants were flying over the sea, silent as dusk, to their roosts in the cliff.

The straight wavelets of the rising tide were moving across the rock pools below the cleft, where under green and purple laver-weed crabs and prawns were stirring to feed. The weed, so placid before, was kicked and entangled by the searching otter. The crab he climbed out with was bitter, and leaving it, he swam into deep water."

THE SHAPE OF THE CLIFFS

The pronounced headland seen to the east is called the Foreland. The long, steep seaward slope hangs above a short sea cliff, very similar to the North Walk. Such cliffs are typical of the north coast of Exmoor. Where their crests dip inland these coastal ramparts are known as 'hog's backs'. How have these unusual cliffs evolved?

Hog's back cliffs

There must be a strong link between the local geological structure, which is dominated by beds of rock dipping inland, and the hog's back cliffs of this coast. Hog's back cliffs can be regarded as particularly steep escarpments. On the Exmoor coast, the inland, south-facing slope roughly relates to the bedding planes (the dip slope), whilst the seaward-facing slope is the scarp face; descending to the sea across the scarp edge of the beds. This association is hinted at in the thumb-nail sketch above. The stepped, tabular appearance of the slope above and below the North Walk is a function of the near-horizontal bedding planes in the rock here, together with widely-spaced jointing which has encouraged the development of massive monumental blocks.

Exmoor hillslopes

Hillslopes characteristically have convex upper sections, short mid-sections where the slope angle is constant, giving straight (rectilinear) slopes, and gentle curving, concave, basal sections. However, here, active erosion by the sea has over-steepened the base, initiating slope failures which have destroyed any concave basal slope which might once have existed. The raw, unvegetated marine cliffs plunge steeply to the shore.

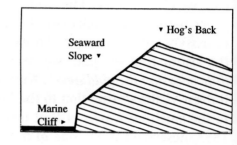

Geological control of slopes?

A feature of many Exmoor slopes, including the seaward slope crossed by the North Walk, is that they have comparatively long straight (rectilinear) mid-sections. Although the actual angle of this straight section may vary according to rock type, these long straight slopes are found on all types of rock along the coast. For example a similar seaward slope can be recognised on the coarse grits of the Foreland. Straight slopes also seem to have developed irrespective of local rock dip. Beds along the North Walk dip gently inland (7 degrees), yet the long, straight, seaward slope on the Little Hangman has an inland dip of up to 40 degrees. It seems, therefore, that the history of these straight seaward slopes is more complex than one of simple geological control. How else could seaward slopes have evolved?

SEAWARD SLOPES   an ice age relict?

Three snapshots of the history of the coast suggest one way in which the seaward slopes might have formed (see also page 44).

1 125,000 years ago   WARM (INTERGLACIAL) CLIMATE similar to present.
Cliffs cut by a sea level some few metres higher than at present.

2 18,000 years ago   COLD (GLACIAL) CLIMATE similar to tundra today.
Sea level has fallen to minus 120 metres with growth of ice sheets.
U.K. ice sheet reaches south to site of Swansea. Bristol Channel dry
tundra plain. Cold (*periglacial*) environment on Exmoor. Abandoned
former sea cliffs attacked by frost activity and degraded to form
steep, straight slopes with thin frost-debris cover (*head*).

3 Present Day   WARM (INTERGLACIAL) CLIMATE.
Most ice sheets melt. Sea level returns to near interglacial level.
Waves cut new cliffs, steadily eroding the seaward slope.

A complex history

In practice the shape of the cliffs must be the result of a complex mixture of the
influence of geological structure, present slope and marine processes and a collection
of relict landforms inherited from a cold past and only partly destroyed by present-
day processes.

The sequence of events proposed above has been repeated many times, with sea
level revisiting old shorelines during interglacials, only to retreat again at the onset
of the next glaciation. This could further complicate the story.

4 ALONG THE NORTH WALK

Exmoor cliffs.   John Presland (1917)

"This to me is one of the charms of walking along these lonely high cliffs: you must go alone, and if not alone, then with a companion who will stop often and stand quietly, and you will see birds from beautiful and unfamiliar angles; below you, showing the broad stretch of their wings and the marking of their backs, or in the level of your eye, so that you can see the distinctive shape of their head and beak, their flight and their movements.

To see two buzzard hawks above a blue sea, circling below you, and then rising higher and higher in a great sweeping spiral, their wings taut till they have the upward curve of a bow, and motionless as they ascend, save for an occasional broad beat as they come, perhaps to what airman call a 'pocket' in the air, and so up until they are two specks against the dazzling brightness of the sky, and you can no longer look at them - this is to me pleasure and occupation enough for a long summer morning."

North Walk   John Ll. W. Page (1895)

"For more than a mile this wonderful pathway is cut in the face of a sheer mountain declivity, in places indeed a precipice. Here and there screes and boulders, red and gray and orange, covered for the most part with lichen or tendrils of ground ivy, lend splashes of vivid colouring to the hillside. Above tower those singular rock masses, the natural bastions of the valley, lying just inside."

As you walk westwards notice how, in places, the seaward slope is broken by outcrops of bare rock or hillside 'tors'. Pause at the tor where sandstone slabs project directly out from the path. This favourite Victorian viewpoint can be readily identified from the lithograph opposite which was "Drawn from Nature and on stone" by W. Spreat c 1850.

Castle Rock, in the immediate foreground. is another 'tor'. John Ll. W. Page (1853) described these rocks as reminiscent of Land's End granite. Elsewhere he speaks of "a rock pile for all the world like a Dartmoor Tor." This similarity is not fortuitous. How do these tors form?

16

COASTAL TORS

Any outcrop of upstanding solid rock with conspicuous joints, standing above the surrounding land surface may be called a tor. They may develop on the crest of a hill, such as Castle Rock, directly ahead, or they may be hillside tors (viewpoints 4 and 7). In both cases they are exposed by the removal downslope of surrounding less resistant, often more closely jointed, material.

The Development of Tors

The most important stage in tor development probably takes place underground, for the way that rocks will behave once exposed will largely depend upon the degree to which they have already been disintegrated and weakened by underground weathering. Rocks are particularly susceptible to weathering along their joints. Those rocks (W) with many joints and planes along which weathering can penetrate, will already be partly decomposed or decayed by the time they are exposed at the surface. Rocks which afford few avenues for the penetration of weathering (R), will be resistant rock outcrops when exposed. Local sandstones tors and granite tors look alike because both are hard and have similar, widely-spaced joints.

Tors in the present climate

A second critical factor in tor development is the rate at which the sound rock is exposed. If rocks are being rotted by weathering faster than the resulting material is eroded, then the depth of weathered mantle will gradually increase and, it can be argued, tors will not be exposed. Such conditions are described as 'transport-limited' because it is the rate of transport which is limiting the speed with which slope processes can operate. Under present climatic conditions in southern England, slope transport on well-vegetated slopes is slow and therefore, except on very steep faces, slopes are usually 'transport-limited' and not conducive to the exposure of fresh tors. It is probable, therefore, that many tors are fossil features inherited from a time when different slope processes dominated.

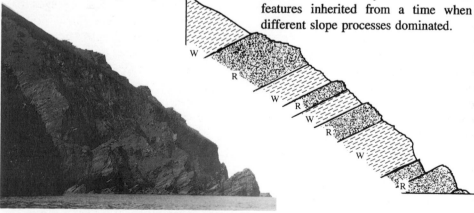

18

▲ A typical tor; Castle rock. Engraving by J. Lowry after T. Allom (1830).

Tors in a periglacial climate

To produce tors, slope processes must remove the weathered mantle faster than it is being replaced by decomposing rocks. If rock removal is limited only by the rate at which it can be weathered, then the slope is described as 'weathering limited'. Such conditions existed in the *periglacial* (tundra) environment of North Devon during the last glaciation (see page 44).

At that time mechanical rock disintegration by freeze-thaw activity was fast, but the rate at which the resulting mantle of debris was swept downslope by mass movements was even faster. New sound rock was constantly being exposed and new tors created. When the climate 'finally' ameliorated (about 10,000 years ago), mass movement suddenly became much less effective. Tors already exposed, persisted as relicts, mute monuments to a cold past.

Straight slopes

The tendency towards straight, rectilinear slopes on many local hillsides, including the seaward slopes, also seems to have been a product of periglacial conditions. It has been suggested that when the climate was harsh, rocks projecting through the mantle of fragmented hillside debris would be more susceptible to frost action than those buried beneath the waste mantle. In this way there could be a progressive removal of irregularities and a uniform slope could develop. Thus, even sound rock, such as tors, would be subject to destructive frost action, but if resistant enough, could persist for some time, standing proud of the general slope. The photo (page 18) shows tors projecting from the seaward slope beneath Highveer near Heddon's Mouth. The slope angle represents the limiting angle of stability of the debris mantle, which in turn is related to the size and angularity of the debris and the amount of water it contains.

19

5 THE VALLEY CENTRE

After a few more yards, the path swings away from the sea. For Victorian visitors following the North Walk out of Lynton or Lynmouth, this would have been their first arresting entry into the Valley of Rocks. Walk into the valley a few metres and, with your back on the sea, consider how you might have felt in this place, 100, 1,000, 18,000, 125,000 years ago.

Of Druids

"The Valley of Stones... is so awefully magnificent that we need not hesitate in pronouncing it to have been the favourite residence of Druidism."
(Rev. Richard Polwhele, c 1793)

"The central part of the valley contains several circles of stone about forty feet in diameter, probably Druidical remains."
(Cooke, 'Topographical Description of Devonshire, 1810)

Some of the standing stones can be seen below in the lithograph by G. Rowe (c 1845), but by 1854 a local landowner, Charles Bailey, was complaining of the building of stone walls and fences, and the opening of quarries in the valley during recent years, and added *"worse than either, the removal of immense Druidical stones and circles which formed its peculiar and striking interest, for the purpose of selling them for gate posts."*

A place to think that troubles were not?

"The valley is a green rough-sided hollow, bending at the middle, touched with stone at either crest, and dotted here and there with slabs in and out the brambles. On the right hand is an upward crag, called by some the 'Castle', easy enough to scale, and giving views of the Channel. Facing this from the inland side and the elbow of the valley, a queer old pile of rocks arises, bold behind one another and quite enough to affright a man, if it were only ten times larger. This is called the 'Devil's Cheese-ring' or 'Devil's Cheese-knife', which means the same thing, as our fathers were used to eat their cheese from a scoop.... but all the middle of the valley was a place to rest in; to sit and think that troubles were not, if we would not make them. To know the sea outside the hills, but never to behold it.... And then to fall asleep, and dream that the fern was all asparagus."

(Jan Ridd's description; in 'Lorna Doone', R.D. Blackmore, 1869)

Or a bitter and inhospitable spot?

"The Castle Rock stands at the mouth of the Valley of Rocks, about which so much has been written, which has been compared with an amphitheatre of giants, or the scene of some titanic conflict, where the huge granite (sic) crags and boulders have been torn up and tossed about by supernatural and terrific forces. In honesty I must admit that this seems to me an exaggeration. Any walker who goes with this in his mind must, I think, be disappointed; the place is wild enough, a bleak, bare, waterless dip in the high lands, without tree or stream to soften it, except in a stone fold, a winter shelter for sheep, where a few twisted and stunted alders exist stubbornly;.... There are hut-circles of the neolithic age in the valley, though many of them have been destroyed by the people who live around, to build the walls of their own cottages; but the oft repeated fantasy of this valley as the haunt of Druid rites seems to me, not only unsupported by evidence, but without justification, in the formation of the valley or the wilderness of the rocks.

Brown under the sunlight, shadeless and glaring, when a blistering north-easter is blowing down it, the Valley of Rocks is a bitter and inhospitable spot; I have been glad to go into the sheep-fold and crouch under the lee of the stone wall for a moment's respite from the wind and the stinging particles of sharp dust that it flung in my face as I battled up the road."

(John Presland, 1917)

Overleaf. The Valley of Rocks, Linton. Lithograph by W. Spreat (c 1850) ▸

A landscape fit for a witch

For nineteenth century visitors, the western end of the North Walk made a dramatic entrance into the heart of the Valley of Rocks. However, the path was early extended to a viewpoint at the top of Castle Rock.

"The industry of a poor old man named Norman, has rendered easy the ascent to the very top of the centre rock, overhanging the sea, called Castle Rock" (Thomas Henry Cooper, Guide to Lynton & Lynmouth, 1853)

Here, Mr Norman fashioned a rude hut from which his wife, Aggie, would provide hot water and the like for picnics. By all accounts Aggie, perhaps sensing the commercial advantage of role playing in this intensely theatrical setting, became more eccentric as time went by, elaborating on the myths and tales of earlier local 'wise women', until a visit to the 'white witch' on Castle Rock became part of the visitor's Lynton itinerary. Aggie Norman died at the age of eighty-three in 1860.

R.D.Blackmore's Lorna Doone was published in 1869. Those wishing to find local inspiration for Blackmore's characters have no problem in identifying Aggie Norman as the role model for Mother Meldrum, the witch visited by Jan Ridd in the Valley of Rocks. In the book, her den is located on the other side of the valley beneath the Devil's Cheesewring.

"Now Mother Meldrum kept her winter in this vale of rocks, sheltering from the wind and rain within the Devil's Cheese-ring; which added greatly to her fame, because all else for miles around, were afraid to go near it after dark, or on a gloomy day. Under the eaves of lichened rock she had a winding passage, which none that ever I knew of durst enter but herself. And to this place I went to seek her, in spite of all misgivings upon a Sunday in Lenten season, when the sheep were folded." (Jan Ridd visits Mother Meldrum in 'Lorna Doone')

Part of the charm that Lorna Doone has on the district, used to advantage by the tourist industry, must be, as John Presland wrote in 1917,

"The admirable sense of locality and the art with which Blackmore has so identified his persons of fiction with the actual places till we no longer dissociate them .....and speak of Lorna and John Ridd as if they had an actual existence;"

◄ The summit of Castle Rock.
Seen from the southern side of the valley, the portal takes the shape of the white witch or white lady.

6 CLIMBING CASTLE ROCK   an optional diversion!

You might like to make a brief diversion from the main walk to emulate Robert Southey, who climbed Castle Rock *"with some toil"* before the path was cut. The summit is a special place to be on a misty morning or to sit watching the channel with an Atlantic evening sun.

"On the summit of the highest point of the hill, two large stones inclined against each other form a portal; here I laid myself at length - a level platform of turf spread before me about two yards long, and then the eye fell immediately on the sea - a giddy depth. After closing my eyes a minute, it was deeply impressive to open them upon the magnificent dreariness, and the precipice and the sea."
(Robert Southey, 1799)

The summit portal (above) drawn by Elizabeth Pheni Spiers on a summer visit in 1847

Feral goat on Castle Rock ▶

In a different mood, near the summit you will find some rippled sandstone. There you could stand bare-foot on the floor of a warm Devonian sea; or finger some slickenside (page 11) to sense the way the beds were sliding.

25

Goats and Castle Rock

"She (Mother Meldrum) pointed to the castle-rock, where upon a narrow shelf, betwixt us and the coming stars, a bitter fight was raging, a fine fat sheep, with an honest face, had clomb up very carefully to browse on a bit of juicy grass, now the dew of the land was upon it. To him, from an upper crag, a lean black goat came hurrying, with leaps, and skirmish of the horns, and an angry noise in his nostrils. The goat had grazed the place before, to the utmost of his liking, cropping in and out with jerks, as their manner is of feeding. Nevertheless he fell on the sheep with fury and great malice.........the goat flung his heels up and rushed at him, with quick sharp jumps and tricks of movement, and the points of his long horns always foremost, and his little scut cocked like a gun-hammer.

I (Jan Ridd) ran up the steep of the rock.....and I hoped almost to save him. But just as my head topped the platform of rock, I saw him flung from it backwards, with a sad moan and a gurgle. His body made quite a short noise in the air, like a bucket thrown down a well-shaft, and I could not tell when it struck the water, except by the echo among the rocks.

So wroth was I with the goat at that moment (being somewhat scant of breath, and unable to consider), that I caught him by the right hind-leg, before he could turn from his victory, and hurled him after the sheep, to learn how he liked his own compulsion." (Lorna Doone; 1869)

Alluding to goats in the 17th century setting of Jan Ridd's visit to Mother Meldrum seems good use of local atmosphere since wild goats have had a long association with the Valley of Rocks. However, it is interesting that goats had been removed from the valley some years before Blackmore wrote Lorna Doone. In a guidebook of 1853 Cooper remarks, *"Formerly wild goats were encouraged in the valley, but some years since it was found necessary to destroy them, as they killed so many sheep by butting them over the adjacent cliffs."*

Feral goats did not reappear in the valley until about 1897 when some were released from Sir Thomas Hewitt's Lynton estate. Feral goats had mixed fortunes during the twentieth century, but their traditional links with the Valley of Rocks and their tourist attraction ensured that whenever extinction threatened, fresh goats were introduced, the current variety being Cheviot.

In time descend Castle Rock and make your way towards the Devil's Cheesewring.

7 THE DEVIL'S CHEESEWRING

Crossing the valley towards the Devil's Cheeswring, pause at the location from which the sketch for the lithograph below was made.

For this hillside tor to be exposed as suggested on page 18, we must imagine this slope clothed in less-resistant well-weathered rock to a depth at least as thick as the tor is high. What process could remove so much rock and where has all this material gone?

Is this process still active today? A crude measure of this would be the recognition of some change since the lithograph (left) was published by G. Rowe *circa* 1830. Any changes of note?

If you explore under the eaves of lichened rock and discover Mother Meldrum's den and the winding passage where none durst enter but herself, it would be of considerable local interest!

The overhang is created by less resistant beds of pale limestone, rich in fossil shells.

A fossil landscape?

The Cheesewring today and that sketched in 1830 shows, give or take a little artistic licence, little change. Well-vegetated slopes and lichen-covered rocks give the impression of an inactive landscape. This is misleading, for there are unseen processes active wherever air and water penetrate the soil. However, most of this weathering is chemical, and often the resulting solutes are removed in ground water without any apparent change in the appearance of the hillside. Of course, when slopes are water-saturated, undercut at the base or weathered to the point of disintegration then catastrophic landslips and slope failure do occur. But at the present time, the average downslope movement of soil and rock debris is very slow. Soil creep is measured in a few mm a year.

Scenery on the move

Conditions were very different 18,000 years ago. Then, Exmoor was a tundra-like wilderness with a mean annual air temperature about 10^0C. colder than today (see page 44). At that time mass movement of soil and hillside rock debris, even down quite gentle slopes, was much faster (in the order of 10-100 mm a year).

Why was slope transport so much more effective in those days?

* In the 'arctic' climate the ground was permanently frozen (permafrost), only the top metre or so briefly melting out each summer (the active layer). Permafrost provided a barrier to the downward infiltration of water into the ground

so that in summer the active layer became extremely moist and unstable with high pore pressures.

* Permafrost acted as a lubricating surface over which the active layer could easily flow, sludging downslope in an unsorted mess of debris of all sizes. This process is called *solifluction* (or more correctly *gelifluction*).

* Freeze-thaw activity detached fresh rock each winter and frost-heave caused the downhill movement of this debris under the influence of gravity.

Solifluction was largely responsible for the unclothing of tors such as the Devil's Cheesewring. The transported debris is called '*head*'. Here the form of the ground suggests that 'plumes' of head oozed down between the tors and fanned out to collect in depth on the gentler slopes of the valley floor.

Stopping the Train

Once exposed, the tors themselves were subject to frost action. Angular blocks prised from the extensive crags on the north side of the valley collected at the base of the slopes as steep screes which remain today. Rocks liberated from isolated hillside tors such as the Cheesewring, were embedded in the head and rafted downslope. Trains of angular boulders streaming downslope mark the decay of each tor. When the climate ameliorated (10,000 years ago) and solifluction ceased to be important, these trains stopped in their tracks. They remain on the hillside today 'frozen in time'.

The Valley of Rocks from above Duty Point (1988). Note the odd smooth grassy shoulder of land on Duty Point, marked X and referred to later. Can you identify your present position from this photograph?

8 WRINGCLIFF BAY

another optional diversion!

Before walking to the next viewpoint you might like to be involved in a mild unresolved controversy. The route of the river which carved the Valley of Rocks is clear, but where did the valley go next? Did it continue along the coast, through the vale at Lee Abbey and join the sea further west (following 9, 10 and 11 on the rear cover map), or did it plunge down into Wringcliff Bay? (8 on page 29).

If this problem intrigues you, a short diversion could be made here to examine a nearby cliff face for clues as to whether a river once entered Wringcliff Bay. The soft cliff face at the back of the bay can be viewed from the top of the zig-zag path which snakes down to the shore, or from the beach itself. The fine sandy beach and rock-pooled foreshore are covered at high tide.

◄ The zig-zag path. Note the human scale in both photos.

▼ Massive boulders flanking Wringcliff Bay, seen from Castle Rock. Most are remnants of cliff landslides precipitated by waves undercutting the base of the cliff.

The path to Wringcliff Bay is the lower of the two footpaths continuing westwards on the seaward side of the surfaced road. The upper path (avoiding the diversion) leads directly, after 200 metres, to viewpoint 9. Pause to look back up the valley where the path turns abruptly uphill towards a lodge on the road.

The Cliffs of Wringcliff Bay

The high cliffs which flank **Wringcliff Bay** are not all composed of solid rock. In the face close to the zig-zag path the rock looks much weaker and less consolidated. Some of this is obscured by vegetated landslip material, but where landslips have exposed the 'true' cliff behind, its nature becomes clearer. It is composed of angular stones, set in an unconsolidated matrix of finer debris, mainly silts and clays. Where did this loose material come from?

A loose head?

This jumble of seemingly unsorted stones from the Lynton Beds, is a typical *head* deposit and in places is over 60 metres thick. Today, this head is relatively stable and can even sustain cliffs with short-term stability. However, during periglacial episodes of the Devensian cold stage (see page 44), when these deposits were most likely laid down, the head would have been accumulating as sludgy debris flows. Within this water-saturated mess, any elongated stones would gradually become aligned within the flow so that their orientation reflected the direction of movement of the debris within which they were embedded. This preferred orientation has persisted to this day and can be used to trace the original direction of travel of the head. By plotting the compass direction of the orientation of a large sample of the stones here, it can be shown that the head came straight out of the Valley of Rocks. This, then, is where the debris, soliflucted from the valley sides to expose the Devil's Cheesewring and other tors, finished up.

Young head on old shoulders

Viewing the cliff face in detail reveals that the head was deposited in a pre-existing V-shaped defile between shoulders of older solid rock. This suggests that prior to the Devensian cold stage (responsible for the head infill), a stream leading from the Valley of Rocks, cut a deep valley into Wringcliff Bay. But is that the final answer to the controversy concerning where the Valley of Rocks led? No river deposits have ever been found, although the valley floor itself is buried somewhere beneath the present beach (F).

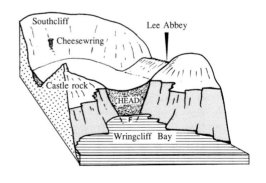

Now make your way back up the cliff and walk to viewpoint 9

9 VIEWPOINT

A landscape filtered through art

The quotations used in this walk sometimes reflect dissimilar responses to the same landscape. The same may be said of the images. Four interpretations of the same view, all drawn from a vantage point close to viewpoint 9, are illustrated in this booklet. Compare that on the front cover with the one on pages 22/23 and those shown opposite.

A romantic vision

Mention has been made of the development of the Lynton district in the early nineteenth century in response to the demands of scenic tourism associated with the Romantic movement. Nineteenth century visitors sought a sense of harmony between themselves and nature and expected a profound intuitive experience from this communion. Most of the illustrations are from this period. They pay homage to nature, seek an emotional response to the drama of this landscape, and stress the human dimension either by the inclusion of pastoral scenes or by including foreground figures, thus implying the presence of the viewer.

The extent of emotional involvement varies. Perhaps a measure of this is the degree to which the dramatic elements in this landscape have been 'intensified'? Compare the illustrations with the real(?) view (the landscape as perceived by you!). The two illustrations on the opposite page provide an interesting contrast. In the 1847 sketch, the drama is heightened by a theatrical enhancement of those elements of the prospect which excite. As a landscape sketch it might be considered to have reached the point of caricature?

A pre-romantic view

The eighteenth century (1790) print opposite, is the earliest of the four illustrations, and is the only one which could be said to reflect a pre-romantic view. The toppling rocks, in those days called the Valley of Stones, give the sense of the topography but, of the four, this is the only illustration which doesn't use the overhanging cliffs to enhance the drama. In this print the valley appears to be at sea level. Pictorial composition was of cardinal importance and the scene has been marshalled to emphasis an orderly series of receding planes. The landscape is depicted as a barren wilderness, devoid of human association except for the ships which one suspects were put there to ensure that we recognised the sea.

A twentieth century filter

An extension of this exercise would be to examine the way that twentieth century art for tourists has filtered the view. Try looking through a postcard display or so in Lynton or Lynmouth. One might suspect that there is a conspiracy to forget the 20th century!

Castle Rock & the Devil's Cheesewring (Mrs E. Pheni Spiers, 1847) opposite ▲
The Valley of Stones, near Linton in Devonshire (Anon c1790)   opposite ▼

The VALLEY of STONES, near Linton in Devonshire

33

10   LEE ABBEY

From viewpoint 9 climb the short but steep footpath up to the surfaced road by the small roadside lodge and turn west along the road. After some 200 metres pause at the entrance to Lee Abbey. An old manor house stood on this site, occupied by the Wichehalse family from 1628 to 1713, initially because plague threatened their Barnstaple home. The present 'Abbey', a mansion of no ecclesiastic origins, was built in 1850 for Charles Frederick Bailey, incorporating elements of the old manor. It was later a hotel before becoming a Christian retreat and conference centre. The disapproval of the Abbey architecture by past critics seems, today, more an occasion for a smile than serious debate.

What the critics said

"We pass through the Valley of Rocks, and shortly afterwards arrive at a modern building of very heterogeneous and questionable architecture, which my Guide-Book informs is called Lee Abbey, and which, fortunately for one's time and temper, is not a show-place."
(George Tugwell, 1863)

"It was never the site of a monastic foundation. It is only a melodramatic abbey".
(Murray Handbook, 1872)

"Sumptuous, ham-fisted Gothic" is how Nicolas Pevsner described it in 1952, but this was somewhat softened in the 1989 edition (The Buildings of England; Devon, Cherry B. & Pevsner N.), which added that it was *"sensitively adapted and extended as a conference and residential centre for the Lee Abbey Fellowship by Scarlett, Burkett Associates, from 1966."*

Whatever your views on the architecture, the setting is superb. Notice we are again in a wide sweeping streamless valley. Is this a continuation to the west of the Valley of Rocks, or is it perhaps another valley which once ran eastwards into Wringcliff Bay? The map opposite indicates the local distribution of gently sloping shoulders, any of which might be remnants of former valley sides. The incomplete nature of the surviving evidence means that a variety of interpretations can and have been made.

Lee Abbey; a valley going west?

Over long periods, river beds usually become roughly graded, so that long-profiles (silhouettes drawn from source to mouth) give a concave slope, steepest at the source and becoming gentler downstream. If only fragments of an ancient river system have been preserved, then one way of testing a former connection would be to see if surviving remnants fit into a smooth long profile. The first serious test of this idea on the Lyn system was by Simpson in 1953. He demonstrated that the upper tributaries of the East Lyn, the Valley of Rocks, the Lee Abbey valley and a further fragment at Crock Point, could all be joined by a curved long profile which might represent the former valley floor.

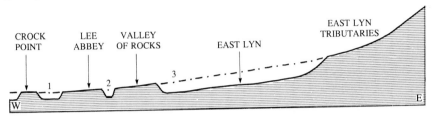

Ideally, the long-profile would have looked something like the crude sketch above. However, in practice the remnants sloped at steeper angles and in odd directions. Such irregularities were explained as subsequent landform modifications as the valley was gradually dismembered by coastal erosion, first at Lee Bay (1), then at Wringcliff Bay (2) where the river, then only recently captured by the sea, could have been responsible for cutting the V-shaped notch previously noted at Wringcliff Bay; before the final capture took place at Lynmouth (3), leaving the whole of the Valley of Rocks dry.

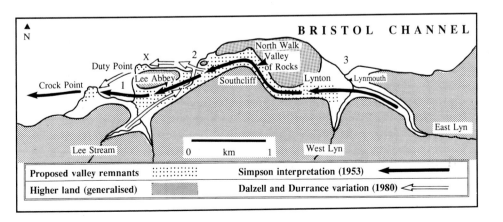

35

Lee Abbey; a valley going east?

Simpson's interpretation (page 35) was based on a long profile surveyed across the ground surface. As we have seen, in places there are thick deposits of head which overlie the solid rock and mask what would have been the floor of the original valley. This makes the survey's accuracy suspect. A later survey by Dalzell and Durrance (1980), used electrical resistance meters to plot the depth of head and locate the buried floor of solid rock (see below).

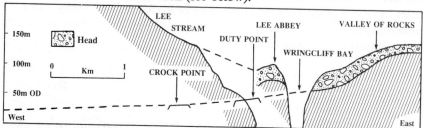

These results suggested to Dalzell and Durrance that the Valley of Rocks (East Lyn) stream could not have continued over the higher rock col of Lee Abbey, and they therefore favoured a route out through Wringcliff Bay, clipping Duty Point (X on the photo on page 29) and continuing across Crock Point. They also suggested that the Lee stream once flowed east over the Lee Abbey col (against the present gradient) to join the west-flowing Valley of Rocks stream at Wringcliff Bay. The Lee tributary would have joined the main stream at an acute angle and then doubled back upon itself to flow westwards. Subsequently, a sequence of captures by coastal erosion, much as proposed by Simpson, could eventually dismember the river system to form the dry fragmented remnants we recognise today.

Where do we go from here?

Sufficient uncertainty remains to ensure that controversy continues. Indeed concrete evidence is tenuous enough to allow scope for healthy speculation, unencumbered by too restrictive a framework of fact! With a good map and the relevant papers (page 45) you could construct a theory or so of your own.

And what of the glacial theory? (Stephens 1966)

If an ice sheet did abut against the Exmoor coast during maximum glaciation, associated glacial deposits (*tills*) have yet to be found. Evidence drawing attention to the similarity of the Valley of Rocks to known meltwater channels elsewhere is also suspect because the valley shape owes much to subsequent modifications, in particular the deep head infills. Unless more concrete evidence emerges the idea of meltwater channels associated with an ancient glaciation must remain intriguing but unsubstantiated speculation.

11 LEE BAY

From Lee Abbey continue west some 400 metres until you reach a toll house (for cars). A small tea cottage (open in season) lies a short distance ahead and may tempt a diversion. Otherwise, turn right down the lane towards the beach. On the right is a small, free museum to the memory of Ursula Winifred Kay, a local naturalist. Just beyond is Pelton House, which once housed a 'Pelton wheel' for a small hydro-electric power station.

The lane follows a small gorge cut by the Lee Stream into a thick terrace of head deposits. Overlooking the beach are the remains of old lime kilns. Limestone from South Wales was landed here from 50-tonne ketches and burnt to make quicklime, once used locally as mortar for building and for liming the local acidic soils. One of the kilns has been converted to a chapel which may be entered. The beach is the furthest point on the guided walk.

Just to the right of the path (looking back from the beach) there is a remarkable sequence of sediments exposed in the soft cliff face. Looking closely at the beds and working from the base upwards, can you recognise changes in the shape and size of the sediments as your eye travels upwards? These differences reflect three major climatic fluctuations in the past. The oldest (1) is at the bottom; the most recent (3) is at the top. Use the list below.

3	1 metre of hillwash in the present climate. (The last 10,000 years. Warm climate after last ice age)	**SOIL**
2	20 metres of angular stones embedded in finer material. *HEAD.* (Tundra climate in last ice age, cold peak: 18,000 years ago).	**FROST DEBRIS**
1	10 metres of rounded stones. Upper beds less rounded. Lower beds well-rounded beach pebbles and sand. High sea level. (Probably last interglacial, about 125,000 years ago).	**OLD RIVER BED** **ANCIENT BEACH**

The changing conditions illustrated by these deposits match very well the sequence of climatic events thought to have modified the Valley of Rocks. The graph on page 44 shows the same dramatic events. The Lee Bay raised beach is more fully examined overleaf.

37

The cliff face at Lee Bay

Interpretation of the evolution of the landscape of the Valley of Rocks so far has been based on landform evidence. The cliff exposure at Lee Bay is sedimentological evidence which helps to confirm the landform interpretation - so far so good!

CLIFF FACE	DESCRIPTION	INTERPRETATION

3 Fine soil/subsoil grades down into coarser blocky layer beneath.

Soil creep and hillwash with coarse basal 'lag' deposit? Vegetation has inhibited active mechanical slope processes.

2 Thin finer layer with few stones overlying thick mass of coarse angular stones embedded in a matrix of finer material of all grades. Unsorted and coarse debris shows no evidence of bedding and no obvious break in deposition. Occasional rounded stones found.

Finer head rapidly grades into typical coarse head. Although undated, considered the result of solifluction during permafrost of the coldest part of the Devensian (Dimlington stadial 26-14,000 years ago). Note preferred orientation of stones.

1(b) Complex mixture of well and poorly-rounded stones and gravel beds with sand. Top sand layer has very fine grain size content, with few pebbles.

River deposits. (Lee stream or something bigger?) Complex mixture of beds probably result of fluctuating estuarine conditions. Cap of finest sand could be wind-blown.

1(a) Well-rounded pebbles in a sandy matrix. Pebbles touching each other (clast supported) and naturally cemented. In places well defined beds of pebble or sand.

Raised beach *in situ*. undated but must predate head. Sea last at this level about 125,000 years ago (Ipswichian interglacial), but beach could be older.

0 Rock platform at 7 metres above present sea level cut across folded Devonian rocks.

Rocky shore platform (wave-cut platform) planed by high sea level in past. May be contemporaneous with the raised beach sitting on it, or older.

[A simple aid for the interpretation of Pleistocene deposits in the field (Keene 1982) is available direct from Thematic Trails, see bibliography]

WALKING BACK: Lee Bay to Southcliff

When you have explored Lee Bay, return to the entrance of Lee Abbey (viewpoint 10). From here you may prefer to walk direct to the Valley of Rocks. There is a tea garden in the middle of the valley (where Jan Ridd mused?). Alternatively, with a short stiff climb, you can return along a footpath which follows the southern edge of the valley (Southcliff) and provides a panoramic view of the Valley of Rocks from above and longer prospects up the East Lyn valley.

To follow the Southcliff route, take the track (on the opposite side of the road to Lee Abbey) which climbs gently back west towards the woods. This path eventually leads to Martinhoe and Woody Bay, but after some 350 metres turn back sharp left (east) onto a path signposted to Six Acre Cross and Lynton via Southcliff. The path climbs through a young beech planation (awash with bluebells in May). Ignore side paths, but follow the path which climbs steeply and is signposted for Lynton over Southcliff.

On Southcliff, the low trees, clipped and combed by the wind, are a reminder of winter. Here, where the path runs beside a wall, you can pause, knowing that the rest of the way is downhill. The tors are now at your feet and beyond them, the Bristol Channel.

This landscape is a veritable hands-on museum. Many of the striking landscape features seen on the walk, such as tors, screes, boulder trains and straight slopes, are relict landforms, inherited from a time when this was a tundra landscape. The valley itself is an even older 'fossilised' museum feature.

At the beginning of the walk (page 8) you may have suggested that the human landscape doesn't seem to have changed much either. Yet, recently, the needs of car-based sightseeing have increased pressure for change at an accelerating rate. Before leaving Southcliff you might reflect on what limits, if any, should be put on changes which, after all, are mainly to cater for the needs of 'scenic tourists' like ourselves!

12 SOUTHCLIFF

The human impact

Except for the inevitable modification to the vegetation through grazing, the human impact on the Valley of Rocks before the nineteenth century was small. The outline of a prehistoric field pattern can still be picked out on the near-side slope below you, but little pre-nineteenth century is evident. However, since the 'discovery' of Lynton, the pressures of tourism have introduced changes at a quickening pace, beginning with the engineering works of Mr Sanford's North Walk and more recently epitomised by the car parks, roundabout and traffic of the motor age. The dangers of uncontrolled development impinging on what was once a remote beauty spot were early recognised;

"This wonderful spot has been greatly disfigured at its entrance on the South East, by enclosures made during the present century, in pursuance of an agreement made in the year 1801, between all the then landowners, for an inclosure of the open lands in the manor; but, much to the credit of some of the claimants, the original rugged and picturesque surface of a great portion of the Valley of Rocks has not been disturbed."

(Thomas Henry Cooper, c 1853)

Planning for the future

The Valley today is not only part of Exmoor National Park, but is also designated as part of a Heritage Coast and a Site of Special Scientific Interest. Through it passes both the Somerset and North Devon Coastal Path and the Tarka Trail. Planners have to consider not only how to respond to the increasing numbers of people who wish to visit this valley by car or coach (larger car parks?) but also whether even the present development of the valley is compatible with its scenic status. They have to take into account how people would wish this environment to be conserved. Given planning powers to influence the present or future human impact on this landscape, what would your priorities be?

In this situation, for many people, an internal conflict emerges. On the one hand there is the desire to conserve the natural beauty and drama of this landscape, perhaps with a vision of the valley returning to its "original rugged and picturesque surface", much as described and drawn by the first scenic tourists of the nineteenth century. On the other hand there is the wish to have open and easy access to this "wonderful spot". If this access is for everyone, then this implies all the modern conveniences of roads, coach parks, picnic areas, toilets and paths. Are these two needs incompatible? A plan which does not strike some compromise is unlikely to be successful. What would you do?

A Taste of Time

This morning I at last reached the Valley of Rocks. I sat resting my back against the massive sandstone slabs and looked out from the escarpment which seemed to hang over the great plains to the north. A dark living-mist drifting silently southwards marked the passage of the second herd of reindeer that day. Winter is approaching.

I should have gone south days ago, but the enjoyment of walking through country I knew, made decisions difficult. I had known that this time-travel experiment was irreversible but, like so many before me, was overcome by intellectual inquisitiveness. At least I now know that the system worked, for here I am. Yet, somehow I regret my curiosity; not for what I have experienced but that there was no one to share it with. Although I am to report back by black plastic canister, which should remain secure for the necessary 18,000 years, it is disturbing that no messages or evidence of those who had time-travelled before had ever been found in the twentieth century, despite all the prearranged plans. I dream of a way back.

The sun still has some strength. Across the tundra, towards the Gower, what, in a moment of mental abberation, I took to be the smoke wreaths of Swansea, turned out to be the sun glinting on the edge of the ice sheet which was splaying its snout out onto the dry floor of the Bristol Channel. Further west I got a glimpse of sea and that surprised me for sea level should have been over 120 metres lower than 'normal', than, well.....when I left. That should have put the coast out beyond Land's End. Perhaps the Welsh ice sheet had depressed the earth's crust more than was calculated?

The Valley of Rocks doesn't look so very different from what I remember; more screes and moss instead of grass. A small ephemeral braided stream, fed by melting snow, snakes over the valley floor exposing some terraces of head. Yesterday, I saw playing in a long, pale slide of water, a small, dark flat-nosed animal. I called him 'Tarka Doone'.

[Undated] My engraved report is ready to be placed, as arranged, in a crevice in the Devil's Cheesewring which, it is hoped, will not be affected by solifluction. Whilst cleaning out the crevice the world stopped, for in the crevice was jammed a corroded canister with my name on. The message began. "Welcome to the future. Regret previous data inverted your travel coordinates. Enter new corrected parameters enclosed." Am worried.

[Undated] What day is it? New parameters must be a failure. Still here, although the season seems to have changed. Camped by the Devil's Cheesewring. It looks very stubby, but I think I have a touch of snow blindness. Last night I heard what sounded like rifle shots but was too weak to investigate. In retrospect I think it must be the ground cracking as it freezes for the winter. Drifting in and out of delirium I fear, for yesterday I saw seventeen Woolly Mammoths (extinct long ago), descend the valley side near the Cheesewring, making for Lynton. Also observed a sabre-toothed scimitar cat sitting on a rock smiling at me. No sign of Tarka Doone. Everything gone. Burnt my journal for heat, bar the last page. Going out to feed the cat. I may be gone some time.

* Manuscript from unauthenticated source found in black flask recovered in situ from solifluction material (Wringcliff Bay 1.4.93.).

Finally, continue along the track which descends diagonally across the hillside towards Lynton. Can you identify your position on the photo on page two? After some 400 metres, leave the main path to turn back sharp left towards the Valley of Rocks. The path passes above the cemetery where victims of the 1952 Lynmouth flood are buried, before ending at the National Park picnic / car park area where the walk started.

GLOSSARY: Some key words explained

BEDS. Bands or layers of rock. Most often used to describe sheets of sediments laid down underwater. The surface which separates one layer (bed) of a sedimentary rock from another is called a **BEDDING PLANE** and this indicates a break between phases of deposition.

ERRATIC. A far-travelled stone transported by ice. Helps to distinguish glacial deposits from similar, but locally derived, slope deposits such as head (q.v.).

GELIFLUCTION. A more precise, but less commonly used word for solifluction (q.v.), used specifically for slope processes in areas of frozen ground.

HEAD. Originally a local farming term for any deep, rubbly subsoil. It is now used to describe the mantle of unconsolidated material produced by the action of solifluction.

OROGENY. A major period of earth movements involving folding, faulting and thrusting usually resulting in the formation of mountain chains.

PERIGLACIAL. Literally peripheral to ice masses. Used to describe very cold, arctic-like environments where freeze-thaw rock shattering and solifluction are major processes.

PERMAFROST. Permanently frozen soil occurring in periglacial (q.v.) areas where winter temperatures rarely rise above freezing point. In summer only the top metre or so thaws, whilst the deeper frozen layer acts as a barrier to percolating water. The active layer becomes saturated and oozes down slope; solifluction, (q.v.).

SOLIFLUCTION. The slow downslope flow of surface material and subsoil when saturated by water. It is most effective in periglacial (q.v.) environments where deep-frozen sub-soil (permafrost) may inhibit the percolation of water in the spring thaw. The process creates head (q.v.).

TILL. Material deposited by glaciers or ice sheets. Characteristically an unsorted, unstratified deposit containing far-travelled stones, erratics (q.v.).

TRACE FOSSILS. Fossilised remnants of the action or effects of an organism rather than the organism itself, e.g. worm casts or burrows formed by shells.

WEATHERING. The decay of rocks on, or near, the surface of the Earth, often in the presence of air or water, It is usually the result of either mechanical breakdown (e.g. frost action) or chemical activity (e.g. solution or oxidation).

ACKNOWLEDGEMENTS

As a publishing charity dedicated to encouraging the interpretation and appreciation of the environment, Thematic Trails depends upon the freely given time and expertise of a host of individuals. We particularly thank the following for their help during the preparation of this booklet: Muriel Arber, Angus Bowden, Chris Cornford, Ben Halliday, Jane Koldewey (woolly mammoths, p42), Ernest Mold, Chris Murphy, Shane O'Donoghue and David Kestor Webb (buzzards, p12 and cave photo, p29).

We thank the following for permission to use illustrative material; Cambridge University Collection of air photographs (pages 2, 12 and 29), Devon Library Sevices [Westcountry Studies Library] (pages 17,20,22,27), the North Devon Athenaeum (pages 19,25,33), the Museum of North Devon (fossils, p11) and the Exmoor Museum, Lynton (pages 8,33).

THE PRE-HISTORY OF THE EXMOOR COAST

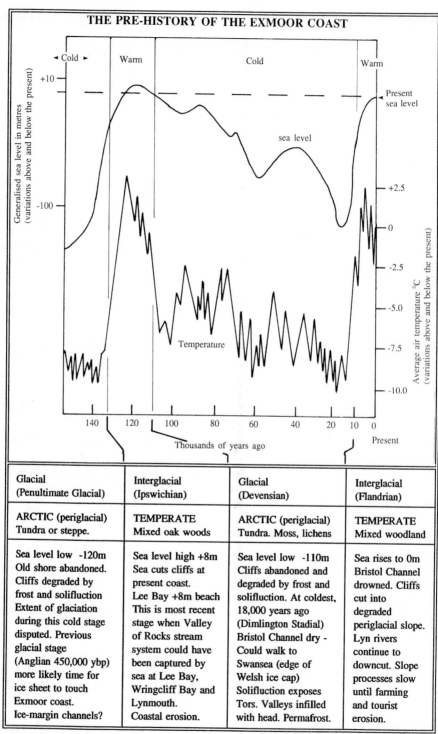

Glacial (Penultimate Glacial)	Interglacial (Ipswichian)	Glacial (Devensian)	Interglacial (Flandrian)
ARCTIC (periglacial) Tundra or steppe.	TEMPERATE Mixed oak woods	ARCTIC (periglacial) Tundra. Moss, lichens	TEMPERATE Mixed woodland
Sea level low -120m Old shore abandoned. Cliffs degraded by frost and solifluction Extent of glaciation during this cold stage disputed. Previous glacial stage (Anglian 450,000 ybp) more likely time for ice sheet to touch Exmoor coast. Ice-margin channels?	Sea level high +8m Sea cuts cliffs at present coast. Lee Bay +8m beach This is most recent stage when Valley of Rocks stream system could have been captured by sea at Lee Bay, Wringcliff Bay and Lynmouth. Coastal erosion.	Sea level low -110m Cliffs abandoned and degraded by frost and solifluction. At coldest, 18,000 years ago (Dimlington Stadial) Bristol Channel dry - Could walk to Swansea (edge of Welsh ice cap) Solifluction exposes Tors. Valleys infilled with head. Permafrost.	Sea rises to 0m Bristol Channel drowned. Cliffs cut into degraded periglacial slope. Lyn rivers continue to downcut. Slope processes slow until farming and tourist erosion.